MW00637995

Measure For Treasure

THE CASE OF THE
BIG CAKE MISTAKE

Written by: Lindy M. Chambers

Edited by: Jennifer Boudart

Illustrated and designed by: Masheris Associates, Inc.

© 1996   Learning Resources, Inc., Vernon Hills, Illinois (U.S.A.)
Learning Resources, Kings Lynn, Norfolk (U.K.)

ISBN: 1-56911-911-2

Printed in the United States of America.

TABLE OF CONTENTS

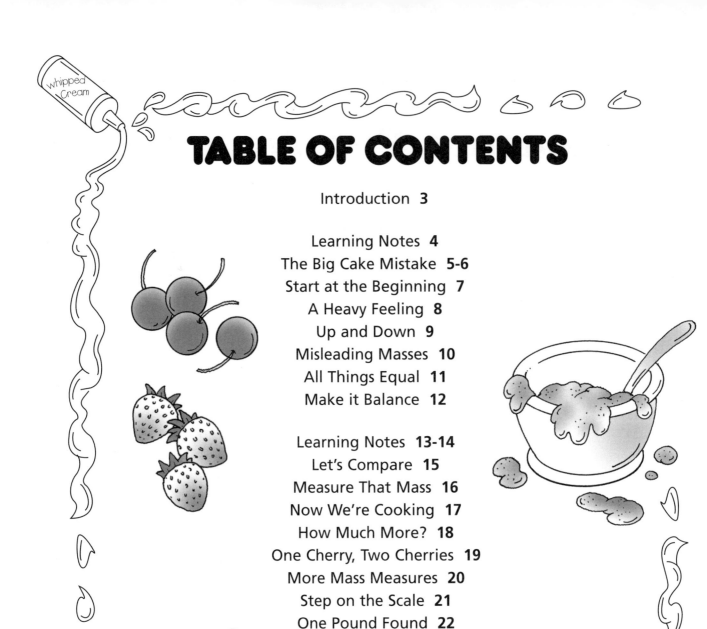

Introduction

Measure for Treasure: Mass engages students in problem-solving activities that explore a variety of measurement concepts involving mass. Students learn about mass measurement while following a story about mixed-up kitchen fun. *Measure for Treasure: Mass* explores mass through comparison, ordering, and measurement with non-standard units (beans, pennies, etc.) as well as standard units (ounces, grams, pounds, etc.) in both the English and metric systems.

Each activity in the *Measure for Treasure* series develops a specific measurement concept. These concepts are in keeping with guidelines known as the *Curriculum and Evaluation Standards for School Mathematics*. Published in 1989 by the National Council of Teachers of Mathematics (NCTM), the *Standards* provide a framework for mathematics instruction in all grade levels. The series also supports the National Research Council's *Science Education Standards*, which stress the combination of scientific knowledge with reasoning and thinking skills.

Students should keep a journal as they progress, to help develop and communicate their conceptual understanding of mass measurement. A blackline master for a "Treasure Log" journal page is provided on page 30 for this purpose. As you complete the activities, look for "Treasure Log" questions and statements; have students respond to these in their logs. Many activities also include mass-related facts. Share these with students to generate further discussion. This discussion, along with completed activities and logs, will provide helpful assessment tools.

Measure for Treasure: Mass activities require the following materials, or suitable substitutions:
- standard metric masses (such as Learning Resources' *Hexagon Metric Masses* [LER 2463])
- gram-unit cubes (such as Learning Resources' *Centimeter Cubes* [LER 2089])
- standard English masses (such as Learning Resources' *Customary Weight Set* [LER 2423])
- balance (such as Learning Resources' *Precision School Balance with Weights* [LER 2420])
- clay
- personal scale

Each book in the *Measure for Treasure* series can be used as a replacement for, or a supplement to, classroom instruction on measurement. *Measure for Treasure: Mass* is designed to be completed as a whole class project. Many of the activities, however, may be adapted for learning centers or instruction at home. Pull out the learning notes and introductory pages (3, 4, 13, 14), and children can work independently through the activities or explore them as teams. The activities in the *Measure for Treasure* series are designed for students in grades K-4; language may be challenging for students in the early grades. Help them as needed, or read the story to them. The activities themselves are appropriate for all students in grades K-4.

A Note To Parents
Although the *Measure for Treasure* series refers to teachers, students, and classrooms, the activities are easily adapted for use at home. As you read through the Learning Notes, put yourself in the place of the teacher. Feel free to substitute common home items for classroom materials when possible. The suggested reading list on page 31 provides additional resources to help you.

Learning Notes

This section introduces children to the concept of mass and how to measure it. Students work with equal and unequal masses and practice using a balance. In doing so, they learn about the properties of mass and the ways in which it is measured.

Page 7—Start at the Beginning
Discuss with students how **mass** can be defined. If appropriate, talk about how it compares with weight. Mass is the amount of matter in an object. Weight is the force of gravity acting on that matter. Your mass never changes. You have the same mass in water, in air, on Mars, or on the moon. But your weight does change in each of these places, because the force of gravity changes. It is not imperative that students clearly see the distinction between mass and weight at this time, just that they are aware there is a distinction. It is likely that, while completing these activities, students will use the terms mass and weight interchangeably.

Page 8—A Heavy Feeling
As students hold different pieces of clay in their hands and attempt to tell which piece has more mass, encourage them to examine the shapes of the pieces they are holding. Students may notice that a flat, large piece may have less mass than a small, ball-shaped piece. This illustrates the point that shape or overall size does not necessarily reflect mass. Students will explore this concept further in later activities.

Page 9—Up and Down
This activity introduces a **balance**. Allow children some time to observe the balance before performing the activity. It may be helpful to model use of the balance for the class, while students describe what you are doing. Be sure they can correctly compare masses on the balance. You also may want to compare the balance and a see-saw to aid students' understanding of the balance's action. Encourage children to explain how the balance works, how it might be used, and how it could be helpful.

Page 10—Misleading Masses
This activity begins a formal discussion of size and shape and their relationship to mass. After completing this activity, students should understand that an object's size or shape is not an indicator of its mass. Very small objects can have large masses and vice versa. Ask students to explain why they think this may occur.

Page 11—All Things Equal
Before students complete this activity, discuss how they might use a balance to see if two objects have equal mass, and the concept of making a balance level. Discuss what it means to have equal mass. Ask if objects must be the same shape and size to have equal mass. Help children select appropriate objects to mass. Be sure they feel comfortable determining when the balance is actually level, using whatever indicators are a part of your balance model.

Page 12—Make it Balance
This activity helps students begin to formalize differences between masses through use of non-standard units. Help students choose two objects to mass and additional objects to use in balancing the masses. If appropriate, discuss with students which types of objects would be best to use for balancing unequal masses. For example, would tennis balls work just as well as beans? (The tennis ball would not be useful if it has too much mass relative to the objects being balanced.) Encourage students to share any balances they achieve.

Measure For Treasure™: Mass © Learning Resources, Inc.

THE BIG CAKE MISTAKE

Ding, dong! Miguel answered his door. His friends stood on the step. "Hi, Miguel. What are you doing today?" asked Tamika. "Do you want to play soccer?"

"I have to help my uncle this afternoon," answered Miguel. "I can play now, though." He told his friends to come in. Then, he ran upstairs to get his shoes. The friends looked around Miguel's kitchen.

Miguel's family owned a bakery. They brought plenty of tasty treats home for visitors... like the cake the friends spotted on the table. It was cut into perfect triangle pieces. Louie decided to take one. Chelsea asked if he was sure it was okay to eat the cake. "Of course," said Louie. "Why else would it be right on the table, ready to eat?" Everyone took a piece. It was very delicious.

Meet Miguel and His Friends

Chelsea Calibration

Ulysses Unit

Vicky Volume

Andy Area

Louie Length

Tara Time

Tamika Temperature

Miguel Mass

5

Miguel came into the kitchen. He groaned and put his hands over his eyes. "Whuff's wongff?" asked Tamika. Her mouth was full of cake.

"You're eating my Uncle Manny's *Magnificent No-Bake Chocolate Mass Cake*!" cried Miguel. "He made it for the inventors' cooking contest! It's this afternoon!" Miguel's uncle had left the cake for him to decorate. Miguel was supposed to sprinkle on some fancy chocolate pieces from the bakery.

The friends felt awful. They had made a big mistake! "Is this contest important?" asked Louie. Miguel told him it was: the winner got a thousand dollars! The friends had to think fast. "Maybe we could make another of these what's-its-name cakes," said Andy. "Your uncle won't know the difference. Do you have the recipe?" Miguel did, but it was the strangest recipe he'd ever seen.

Measure For Treasure™: Mass © Learning Resources, Inc.

START AT THE BEGINNING

Miguel explained that his uncle was an inventor. He made lots of crazy things. "Uncle Manny looks forward to the inventors' cooking contest all year," said Miguel. "To enter, you have to invent a recipe in the laboratory instead of the kitchen. That means using laboratory equipment. This year, Uncle Manny based his ingredients on **mass** to invent a no-bake cake."

"What's mass?" asked Tara. "My uncle says it's a lot like weight," answered Miguel. "When you measure mass, you measure how much stuff makes up an object, like a rock or a chair."

It's Your Turn!
Discuss how you would describe mass. Write three examples of mass. Why might be important to know an object's mass?

1. _____

2. _____

3. _____

A HEAVY FEELING

Tara said, "I understand what you mean, Miguel." She grabbed a lemon and a cherry from the fruit bowl. "Both these pieces of fruit have mass. Hmm... I think they have different masses, though."

"Why do you think so, Tara?" asked Louie. Tara told him she could feel it. "I think this lemon has more mass because it feels heavier in my hand."

It's Your Turn!
Gather some clay. Break it into two pieces. Press the pieces into different shapes. Hold the pieces in your hands. Which piece do you think has more mass? Why?

UP AND DOWN

"There's a way to tell if you're right, Tara," said Miguel. "Luckily, Uncle Manny brought the equipment he used to make his cake." Miguel put a box on the table. He took out something his uncle called a **balance**. It measured mass. Uncle Manny used it to measure his ingredients.

Miguel's friends asked how the balance worked. "Uncle Manny showed me," answered Miguel. "Watch this." He put the cherry in one tray and the lemon in the other tray. Everyone watched what happened. "Tara was right," said Louie. "The lemon has more mass."

It's Your Turn!
Place one piece of clay on your balance. What happens? Place another piece of clay on the other side of your balance. What happens? Which piece has more mass? How do you know?

Treasure Log
Change the shape of your clay pieces. Place them on the balance again. Does the clay's mass change when you change its shape? Why or why not?

MISLEADING MASSES

"Let me try," said Ulysses. He chose a lettuce leaf and a walnut. "I think this lettuce leaf has more mass than this little walnut," said Ulysses. "The lettuce is much bigger."

Ulysses put one object in each tray on the balance. The walnut had more mass than the lettuce! Miguel told Ulysses not to feel bad for guessing wrong. "I guessed wrong on my first try, too," said Miguel. "Uncle Manny said size can fool you when it comes to mass. Sometimes small objects have more mass than big objects."

It's Your Turn!
Compare the mass of three pairs of objects. First, guess which object you think will have the greater mass. Then, place the objects on the balance. Record your results in the table.

Object 1	Object 2	My Guess	My Results

Measure For Treasure™: Mass © Learning Resources, Inc.

ALL THINGS EQUAL

"What would happen if we put two things that have equal mass on the balance?" asked Vicky. "I'll show you," said Miguel. He put one cherry on both sides of the balance. The trays were even in height. "Uncle Manny called the balance **level** when he did this," said Miguel. "It shows the masses on the balance are the same, or equal."

It's Your Turn!
Collect two identical objects, such as two new erasers. Place one object on each side of your balance. What happens? What does this tell you about the mass of each object?

Did You Know?
• One of the earliest known balances was invented about 7,500 years ago in Egypt. That balance was a stick which hung by a cord tied around its middle. By hanging an object from each end of the stick, and watching how the stick dipped, a person could compare the objects' masses.

Measure For Treasure™: Mass © Learning Resources, Inc.

MAKE IT BALANCE

Chelsea had an idea. She reached for a jar of lima beans. Then, she put a piece of lettuce in one tray and a cherry in the other tray of the balance. The cherry had less mass. One by one, Chelsea added beans to the tray holding the cherry. She did this until the balance was level. "Ta-dah!" said Chelsea with a smile. "I've made unequal masses equal!"

It's Your Turn!
Choose two objects with unequal mass. Place them on either end of your balance. Which object has less mass? Collect some smaller objects (beans, pennies, washers, etc.). Try to level the balance by adding your small objects to the correct end of the balance.

Treasure Log
If two objects on a balance have unequal mass, how do you decide which end to add mass to if you want to make the balance level?

Learning Notes

This section introduces students to standard mass units in both the metric and English systems. Students practice massing with these units, and explore their relationships to each other.

Pages 15—Let's Compare
This activity demonstrates the importance of having a unit of mass measurement that can be communicated to and used by other people. Otherwise, students can say an object has a mass of so many beans, but another person who uses beans may achieve a different result. Discuss this with your students and have them suggest solutions to this problem.

Page 16—Measure That Mass
Introduce students to **grams** using standard mass sets and gram unit cubes. Discuss the metric system, and ask students to give examples of other units they know (other metric mass units will be explored in later activities). Encourage students to find the mass of objects using the gram masses. This may be an appropriate time to discuss measurement practices, e.g., zeroing balances and allowing the balance to reach its resulting level by itself rather than stopping it manually.

Page 17—Now We're Cooking
This activity expands on the previous activity. It allows students more practice with measuring mass. As students record their results, this may be a good time to introduce the symbol for grams: (g). *Note:* The ingredients listed in the story are not part of a real recipe. Also, discourage kids from choosing food for this activity, to avoid sanitary problems (the food will not be immediately eaten once measured).

Page 18—How Much More?
This activity can be accomplished in two ways. Students first may find the mass of each object separately, then calculate the difference. Or, they may compare the objects' masses and add masses to the lighter side of the balance. They then can count the masses they added to find the difference. Encourage students to try the activity both ways.

Page 19—One Cherry, Two Cherries
This activity introduces the idea of **replicates**. Students should realize identical objects should have approximately the same mass. Students really only need to do one measurement, then multiply (or add in sequence, in the case of younger children) to find the mass for multiples. However, it is more accurate to find the measurements for several identical objects, then divide to find the mass of a single object. This technique will help reduce measurement error as well.

Page 20—More Mass Measures
This activity introduces another metric mass unit, the **kilogram**. Take up your earlier discussion of kilograms. Introduce the symbol for the kilogram: (kg). Ask students to give examples of things they have seen measured with this unit. Help them choose objects that may have a mass of approximately 1 kilogram for the activity. You will need standard kilogram masses as well. If you wish, you also can introduce tons and drams, and the relationship between all these metric units.

Page 21—Step on the Scale
Introduce students to English units of measure with a bath scale. Students should be familiar with weighing themselves and with the unit **pounds.** *Note:* Some bathroom scales may not be sensitive enough to show a good reading of one pound. Explain students could find their mass with grams on a balance if it was large enough, but for big objects, other types of scales or balances are used. Ask students to give examples of where they have seen things measured in pounds. Introduce the symbol for the pound: (lb).

Page 22—One Pound Found

This activity will give students an intuitive feel for the mass of a pound. Help them select an appropriate object to mass. You also will need a standard kilogram mass for this activity. Encourage students to describe the relationship between a kilogram and a pound (one kilogram is equal to about 2.2 pounds). Most conversions between English and metric units of mass result in decimals; therefore, you only may want to explore relationships between pounds and kilograms and **ounces** and grams (see page 26).

Page 23—Break it Down

This activity may be challenging for students. Have them start with a pound of materials that can be divided easily, such as uncooked pasta. Help students create two 8-ounce masses using their balance. You may wish to model the second half of the activity, which involves further dividing to create a 1-ounce mass. Encourage students to divide one of their 8-ounce masses in half. Confirm they know they have two 4-ounce masses. Students must halve 4 ounces to get a 2-ounce mass, and finally halve 2 ounces to get a 1-ounce mass. Students can pour their materials into sandwich bags to make their own standard mass units. Give students an opportunity to test the accuracy of their work against manufactured masses included with most scales.

Pages 24 and 25—Frosting Fun, Almost There

Students may have difficulty finding objects with similar masses as required for these activities. Remind students that size and shape don't always indicate mass, so selection based on appearance may not be reliable. You may want to have students work in teams or groups. You also may want to set up these activities in a contest format. This will motivate students to search for and mass objects carefully. These activities will provide extensive hands-on practice.

Page 26—Two Great Tastes

If students have made enough homemade ounce masses, they can use them for this activity. Otherwise, supply them with manufactured ounce masses. Students should find 5 ounces represent more mass than 5 grams. One ounce equals approximately 28 grams. Accordingly, students should add grams to make the balance level, and count how many grams and ounces they have to complete the activity.

Page 27—Different but the Same

This activity reinforces the concept that changing an object's shape does not affect its mass. Students can try several variations of this activity to satisfy their curiosity. The amount of explanation you give about this phenomenon will depend on your students' understanding of mass vs. weight and the idea of conservation of matter.

Page 28—At the Contest

Use this activity as an assessment. The five questions can be used as a mini quiz. (*Answers:* 1,000 grams; an ounce has more mass than a gram; metric system; English system; and 20 grams.) You also may want to set up a performance assessment at this time which involves massing an object.

Page 29—Everyone Wins

This activity is a fun way to reward your students and to help them apply what they have learned about mass measurement. Divide children into groups. Review the directions before you begin. Be sure students understand they are going to measure ingredients for a recipe based on mass, and fill in the blanks to indicate how much of each ingredient is needed. Give each group 6 celery stick halves, 1 plastic cup filled with peanut butter, and about 30 raisins. Older students may be concerned that the plastic cup will affect their measurement. Allow them to mass a plastic cup separately and subtract the result from their total for this ingredient.

Measure For Treasure™: Mass © Learning Resources, Inc.

LET'S COMPARE

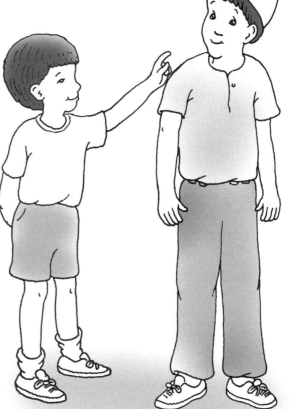

"Excuse me, Miguel," said Andy. "I still don't see how this balance helps measure masses. So far, we have just been *comparing* masses."

"Wait a minute, Andy," said Tara. "I think we *have* been measuring. After all, we can say a lettuce leaf has the mass of one cherry plus 13 lima beans." She pointed to the level balance. "Okay," said Andy. "But how much mass do one cherry and 13 lima beans have?" Everyone looked at Miguel.

It's Your Turn!
Choose an object to place on your balance. Make the balance level by adding multiples of one kind of object (such as beans) to the opposite side. Count how many objects you added to make the masses equal. For example, 10 beans might balance one crayon.

Did You Know?
• The gram is equal to one cubic centimeter of water.

MEASURE THAT MASS

Miguel took a bag of little cubes from his uncle's box. The printing on the bag read: "Standard Gram Cubes."

"My uncle says these cubes are a handy way to measure mass," said Miguel. "Each cube has a mass of 1 **gram**. Grams are part of the metric system. Uncle Manny says the metric system includes different units for making big and small measurements."

Miguel put 13 lima beans on the balance. He added gram cubes to the empty tray. When the balance was level, he counted the cubes. That told him the beans' total mass.

It's Your Turn!

Practice measuring mass with standard gram masses.
Use a balance and standard gram masses to measure the mass of the objects listed in the table. Record your results.
Compare your results with your classmates' results.

Objects	Mass in Grams
10 lima beans	
10 pennies	
10 paper clips	

Treasure Log
Is measuring mass in grams better than measuring mass in beans? Why or why not?

Measure For Treasure™: Mass © Learning Resources, Inc.

NOW WE'RE COOKING

Ulysses was playing with the balance. He found a little drawer. It was filled with round, metal objects. Ulysses showed them to his friends. They noticed all the objects were marked "5g," "10g," "20g," or "50g." Miguel smiled. "I think these are mass units, like the gram cubes," he said. "I bet the 'g' stands for grams and the number stands for how many grams of mass each object has! I think we're ready to start measuring our ingredients!"

They first measured 100 grams of chocolate sprinkles. Miguel put 50 gram cubes and a metal mass unit marked "50g" on the balance. He added sprinkles to the other side until the balance was level.

It's Your Turn!
Measure the mass of five objects using standard gram masses and a balance. Record your measurements in the table below. Don't forget your unit: grams!

Object	Mass in Grams

Name _____ Date _____

HOW MUCH MORE?

The friends were very proud of themselves. They quickly measured the rest of the ingredients, including 200 grams of sliced strawberries, 100 grams of graham cracker crumbs, and 50 grams of coconut flakes. They poured the mixture into a cake dish. Then, they put it in the refrigerator. The recipe said they could frost it after half an hour.

Tara chewed an apple. "Does an apple have more mass than a lemon?" she asked. "Let's find out!" said Miguel. He used the balance and his mass units to check. "This apple has 15 more grams of mass than this lemon," reported Miguel.

It's Your Turn!
Place two objects on a balance. Which object has less mass?
Add standard gram masses to that mass until the balance is level.
Count how many grams you added. The number equals the difference
in mass between the two objects.

Write the difference you measured in sentence form.

Example:
A calculator has 61 more grams of mass than a ruler.

_____

18

ONE CHERRY, TWO CHERRIES

"I wonder if two cherries have twice the mass of one cherry?" asked Tara. "Let's find out!" said Miguel. He put one cherry on the balance. Then, he added gram cubes to the other side until the balance was level. He counted the cubes. Next, Miguel placed a second cherry with the first one. He added gram cubes to level the balance. He counted the cubes again and compared his two numbers.

It's Your Turn!
Find the mass of one marble using a balance and standard gram masses. Then, find the mass of two, three, four, and five marbles. Repeat this activity with another object you choose. Record your measurements in the table below.

Object	Mass of 1	Mass of 2	Mass of 3	Mass of 4	Mass of 5
Marble					

Treasure Log
What did you expect would happen to the mass of the marbles as you increased their number? Were you right?

MORE MASS MEASURES

"Let's make the frosting," said Vicky. Ulysses picked up the recipe. "Uh-oh," said Ulysses. "We need 1 **kilogram** of cocoa powder. Is that a little or a lot?"

Miguel didn't know. Uncle Manny hadn't mentioned kilograms. Maybe a kilogram was a metric unit. And maybe Uncle Manny had one in his box. Miguel took a look. He picked up a metal object. It had much more mass than a gram cube! Miguel read the words printed on the bottom: "1 kilogram (equal to 1,000 grams)." Miguel showed his friends. Chelsea used the new mass to measure the cocoa.

It's Your Turn!
Can you find an object that has a mass of about 1 kilogram? Check the mass of your object on the balance using a kilogram mass. How close are you?

Treasure Log
If there are 1,000 grams in a kilogram, what do you think "kilo" means?

Did You Know?
• In 1875, the International Bureau of Weights and Measures was established. This Bureau created a laboratory in France near Paris. The Bureau uses the laboratory to keep the world's official standard units for measurement, including mass units.

Measure For Treasure™: Mass © Learning Resources, Inc.

STEP ON THE SCALE

"Are there any other mass units we need?" asked Tamika. Ulysses nodded. He said, "I see **ounces** and **pounds**. Uncle Manny wrote a note here... it says ounces and pounds meet contest rules for using English and metric units. If grams and kilograms are metric units, ounces and pounds must be English units."

Miguel looked for ounce and pound mass units in the box. The box was empty! "I have an idea," said Tara. "My mom just weighed me on our bathroom scale. She told me I weigh 52 pounds. Maybe a bathroom scale would help." Miguel found one. Everyone took turns stepping on the scale.

It's Your Turn!
Give examples of where you have seen weight and mass measured in English units. Then, find your weight in pounds on a bath scale. Your teacher will help you.

ONE POUND FOUND

"I weigh 48 pounds," said Chelsea. "I weigh 51 pounds," said Andy. "We need a mass unit that equals just 1 pound," said Ulysses. "The recipe says to measure 1 pound of chocolate chips." The friends wondered where they could find a 1-pound mass.

Miguel looked around the kitchen for ideas. He saw a bag of uncooked pasta. He read the package. It said there was 1 pound of pasta inside! To be sure, Miguel put the bag on the bathroom scale. It showed 1 pound.

It's Your Turn!
Place a 1-pound bag of uncooked pasta or another object your teacher gives you on a bath scale. Does the scale show 1 pound of mass? Now, put your object on the balance. Balance it with a standard 1-pound mass. Balance it with a kilogram mass. How does 1 pound compare to 1 kilogram?

Did You Know?
• Some of the earliest standard units for measuring mass were created in Egypt almost 5,000 years ago. They were made from stone and came in different sizes. These units were used to measure out food, medicine, cloth, and other materials.

Measure For Treasure™: Mass © Learning Resources, Inc.

BREAK IT DOWN

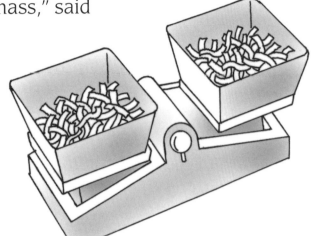

"I found a 1-pound mass," said Miguel. He showed his friends the pasta. Tara noticed some writing along the bottom. She read it out loud: "One pound equals 16 ounces."

Ulysses looked at the recipe. "We need 8 ounces of peanut butter, not 16 ounces," he explained. Miguel snapped his fingers. "We could split the pasta into two equal masses," he said. "That would make 8 ounces and 8 ounces." Miguel added pasta to both sides of the balance until it was level. He poured pasta from each tray into its own sandwich bag. "There!" said Miguel. "We made our own 8-ounce mass units!"

It's Your Turn!
Make two 8-ounce masses from a pound of uncooked pasta. Use standard ounce masses to check your work. Now, make a 1-ounce mass. Your teacher will help you.

Treasure Log
Explain the steps you took to create an ounce from a pound.

Measure For Treasure™: Mass © Learning Resources, Inc.

FROSTING FUN

"Now we have all the units we need," said Ulysses. "We can measure with grams, kilograms, ounces, and pounds." Louie said, "Let's start with pounds first." He used the two 8-ounce pasta masses to measure out a pound of chocolate chips.

It's Your Turn!
Try to find three objects that have a mass near 1 pound. Use your homemade pound unit and the balance to check your guess. Record each object you measure in the table below. Put a check under the answer that matches your results.

Object	More Than 1 Pound	Less Than 1 Pound	Equal to 1 Pound

Treasure Log
Why were the friends able to use two 8-ounce pasta masses to measure one pound of chocolate chips?

Measure For Treasure™: Mass © Learning Resources, Inc.

ALMOST THERE

Next, the kids decided to measure the peanut butter for their frosting. It was messy work! They got as close to 8 ounces as they could. Then, they measured the rest of their ingredients. Miguel mixed everything together. The frosting was done! Tara took the cake out of the refrigerator. "Well, it looks the same as your uncle's cake," said Tara. "Let's hope it tastes the same!"

It's Your Turn!

Try to find three objects that have a mass near 1 ounce. Use your homemade ounce unit and the balance to check your guess. Record each object you measure in the table below. Put a check under the answer that matches your results.

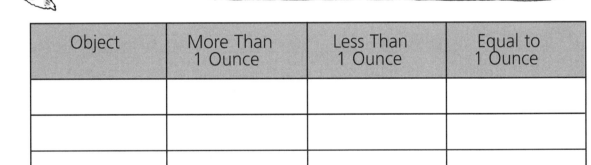

Object	More Than 1 Ounce	Less Than 1 Ounce	Equal to 1 Ounce

Treasure Log
Were all the objects you measured about the same size?
Why do you think this is so?

Measure For Treasure™: Mass © Learning Resources, Inc.

TWO GREAT TASTES

Miguel started to frost the cake. His friends wished they could have a taste, to see if it was as good as the first one. "I really like peanut butter," said Tamika. "I wish we could have added more than just 8 ounces." Louie said coconut was his favorite. "I wish we could have added more than 50 grams of coconut flakes."

"I wonder which unit has more mass, ounces or grams?" asked Tamika. "Let's find out!" said Louie.

It's Your Turn!
Compare ounces to grams on your balance. Place 5 grams on one side of the balance and 5 ounces on the other side. Which side has more mass? Make the balance level. Add up the mass units on both sides. Fill in the statement below.

_____ ounces are equal to _____ grams.

DIFFERENT BUT THE SAME

Next, Tara and Louie decided to make a peanut butter-coconut ball. They measured the same amount of peanut butter and coconut flakes: 50 grams each. They mixed the two ingredients to make a ball. Louie measured its mass: 100 grams. "The shape changed, but the mass didn't," said Louie. "We started and ended with 100 grams."

Miguel finished frosting the cake. He sprinkled on some fancy chocolate pieces. It was time to meet his uncle at the contest. "We'll go with you, Miguel," said Chelsea. "We have to see what happens!"

It's Your Turn!
Measure the mass of a piece of clay using your standard mass units. Then, break it into smaller pieces, or make it a different shape. Measure the clay's mass again. What results do you get? Why do you think this is so?

AT THE CONTEST

Lots of people had come to see the contest. It was very crowded. The kids passed rows of tables with food of all kinds. Miguel saw Uncle Manny waving to him. "You're just in time, Miguel," said Uncle Manny. "The judging is starting." Miguel handed over the cake. Uncle Manny smiled proudly. "Those fancy chocolates are perfect, Miguel," he said. "Maybe when you grow up you can be a smart inventor like me. Maybe you can even make a cake like this!" The kids looked at each other and giggled.

It's Your Turn!
Be a smart mass measurer.
Answer these questions about mass.

1. A kilogram = _____ grams.
2. An ounce has more/less mass than a gram.
   (Circle the correct answer.)
3. A gram is a unit in the _____ system.
4. A pound is a unit in the _____ system.
5. If one object has a mass of 10 grams, 2 of those objects have a mass of _____ grams.

EVERYONE WINS

Uncle Manny's cake was the last to be judged. The judge tasted the cake. She read the recipe. She looked at the equipment. Without a word, she walked away. Everyone waited quietly. The judge stepped up to a microphone. "The winner is Manny Blanco," called the judge, "for his Magnificent No-Bake Chocolate Mass Cake!"

The judge handed Uncle Manny his prize money. Miguel tugged on his uncle's sleeve. "I have something to tell you," whispered Miguel. He explained about the cake mistake, and how they all had fixed it. At first, Uncle Manny frowned. Then he laughed, and said, "You saved the day, kids! I'm going to share my prize with all of you!"

It's Your Turn!
Make your own dessert! Use your balance to find the mass of the ingredients your teacher gives you. Then, fill in the ingredient list. Write how much of each ingredient is needed. Don't forget your mass units.

Ants on a Log

Ingredients:

Directions:
Spread peanut butter in the groove of each celery stick.
Add raisins on top. Enjoy!

Treasure Log

Suggested Reading

Your students may enjoy reading other books about mass. Some appropriate books for students in grades K-4 are listed below.

• Ardley, Neil. **Making Metric Measurements.** New York: Franklin Watts, 1983.

• Arnold, Caroline. **Measurement: Fun, Facts, and Activities**. Illustrated by Pam Johnson. New York: Franklin Watts, 1984.

• Shapp, Martha and Shapp, Charles. **Let's Find Out What's Light and What's Heavy**. New York: Franklin Watts, 1975.

• Spier, Peter. **Fast-Slow, High-Low. A Book of Opposites**. New York: Doubleday & Co., 1972.

• Srivastava, Jane Jones. **Weighing and Balancing.** Illustrated by Aliki. New York: Thomas Y. Crowell Publishers, 1970.

CONGRATULATIONS
ON YOUR EXPLORATIONS WITH MASS!

_____

Treasure Seeker's Name

**Your extraordinary work
has helped us immeasurably!**

Signed:
Chelsea, Ulysses, Tamika, Louie,
Andy, Tara, Vicky, and Miguel